Along the Way Series
With Gary and Anne Marie Ezzo

Preparation for Parenting - Along the Infant Way
Preparation for the Toddler Years - Along the Toddler Way
Growing Kids God's Way - Along the Virtuous Way
Parenting the Middle Years - Along the Middle Years Way
Reaching the Heart of Your Teen - Along the Adolescent Way
Reflections of Moral Innocence - Along the Innocent Way

Reflections of Moral Innocence

Reflections of Moral Innocence

Learning to Communicate Sexual Knowledge with Dignity

STUDY GUIDE

Along the Innocent Way

Gary & Anne Marie Ezzo

Reflections of Moral Innocence

Learning to Communicate Sexual Knowledge with Dignity

Study Guide

International Standard Book Number
ISBN-10: 1-883035-06-6
ISBN-13 978-1-883035-06-8

Printed in the United States of America

Growing Families International
P. O. Box 54 Louisiana, MO 63353

08 09 10 11 — 24 23 22 21 20

Dedicated to:

Our dearly loved friends:
Shawn, Kathy, David and Suzanne

Acknowledgements

As has been the case from the beginning of this series, we have many people to thank for making this presentation possible. Too our wonderful class that sat through the many weeks of video taping, and a special thanks to the GFI staff for their patience, dedication and commitment to the lofty ideal of protecting the sexual innocence of children. We also want to acknowledge and thank Steve and Charlotte Newcomb for assisting us in creating the core curriculum. Finally, a special thanks to Joe and Audrey Werner for their special insights and contribution to this book.

Table of Contents

Preface

Even those who are casual observers of societal trends clearly recognize that much of Western civilization has for many years been on a moral decline. But the slippage has never been so rapid as in the last forty- years. The challenges of this decline has made appropriate sex education of children very difficult. The fact that the subject is so popular is in fact part of the problem.

"Sex Education" officially began in 1964 with the Kinsey report and a new view of sexuality outside the context of marriage and children. Kinsey was credited for having socially separated sex from procreation. Before Kinsey, the titles that reflected the American notion of human sexuality were "God's Life Process" or the "Marital Act" and everything else was know as "Carnal Knowledge."

It is our desire, through this series to put God's design for sexual attitudes and conduct back in the right biblical anthropological context. And while we still use some of the contemporary terminology throughout this book, let it be known that it is done only to stay consistent with our contemporary audience and not an endorsement of Kinsey's concepts or beliefs.

So we ask: "How can we teach our children a biblical view of sexuality when from a very early age they are saturated with details and images that constantly challenge the very concept of biblical purity?" There is an answer. Train those who have access to the hearts of the children – train the parents. No one can do the job better than a rightly trained parent because no one can represent the parents' value system better than themselves. As a parent, you should determine what is morally and biologically appropriate for your children and when they should receive that information. Your willingness to participate in this series and apply the principles will give your children a greater chance to enjoy what God intended them to enjoy –their childhood.

Regarding this small outline guide. It is not intended to be comprehensive. In fact, it serves a limited purpose – to assist the viewer in tracking the general themes of the video presentation. Many of our verbalized statements do appear in this text, but not all our statements are contained. Further we wish to note that the general statistics cited in this series were common at the time of the original presentation. Some of these may have fluctuated up or down over the last decade. However, none to our knowledge have changed significantly from the time of our original presentation and thus no updates were noted in this printed edition.

Finally, we invite you to join the community of parents pursuing like-minded values at GrowingKids.org. Here you can join chat room conversations, browse our parenting library or ask questions. The site is filled with articles, commentary and links to other helpful resources. It is a way for you to connect with a moral community of like-minded values. Come, visit, and browse the site.

Until then, may the Lord bless your faithfulness to the task of raising children with the purity principle in mind.

Gary and Anne Marie Ezzo
Charleston, South Carolina

Reflections of Moral Innocence Session Outlines

Session One

Defining the Problem

I. Welcome

A. Defining Our Title

When we speak of innocence, we are not speaking of the theological aspects of human innocence, which include innocence lost in the Garden of Eden and the ultimate effect of sin on the human race.

The sense in which we use the term innocence refers to a _________ naiveness, the lack of experience with the world, or lack of exposure and defilement.

We believe it is right to let children be ____________ as long as they can, and we believe it is wrong to rush children into adulthood. All of us get only one childhood. What are you doing to protect it for your children? There is no faster way to rob a child of the innocence of childhood than with inappropriate sex education.

Reflections of Innocence is a study in the basic truths of human sexuality, especially the developing sexuality of children. Our views are developed from a biblical perspective. For Christians, there is no other starting point than the mind of God. We understand the mind of God through the Word of God.

B. Our goal is to put _______________ in you – to put courage in parents to step away from the noise of the

Notes

Notes

crowd and listen for God's voice on this matter.

C. We trust that by the end of this series you will have the confidence of knowing:

1. ______________ to communicate

2. ______________ to communicate

3. ______________ to communicate biological truth to your children with biblical values attached

II. The Question

How can we teach our children a biblical view of sex when from a very early age our children are inundated with information that directly conflicts with biblical values and a Christ-centered world-view? That poses a serious dilemma.

A. The answer is twofold. There is the:

1. ________________ side, and

2. ________________ side.

Protecting the sexual innocence of our children involves taking steps to prevent or at least minimize the intrusion of moral perversion in the minds of our children until they are old enough to develop a moral value system that can internally regulate their behavior and their moral decisions.

Preparation not only identifies the process by which the parents communicate moral values to their children, but also how they live out their value system in front of their children.

B. The Goal of Sex Education

The goal of sex education is not to teach your children how to have safe sex, but rather how to be masters of their passions rather than be enslaved to their passions. For most of history, the preparation side of sex education was the only challenge parents faced. Protecting was never an issue. Protection was part of our collective societal obligation until the late 1960s.

But those days are gone. Today, as it was in the day of Nehemiah, we must build with a trowel in one hand and protect with a sword in the other. We must have a new progressive strategy in communicating the facts of life to our children without destroying their sexual innocence.

C. The Warning: Matthew 18:1-7

"At that time the disciples came to Jesus, saying, 'Who then is greatest in the kingdom of heaven?' Then Jesus called a little child to Him, set him in the midst of them, and said, 'Assuredly, I say to you, unless you are converted and become as little children, you will by no means enter the kingdom of heaven. Therefore, whoever humbles himself as this little child is the greatest in the kingdom of heaven. Whoever receives one little child like this in My name receives Me. But whoever causes one of these little ones who believe in Me to sin, it would be better for him if a millstone were hung around his neck, and he were drowned in the depth of the sea. Woe to the world because of offenses! For offenses must come, but woe to the man by whom the offense comes!'"

Notes

Notes

III. The Problem

A. How do you Define Sex?

Attempting to define the parameters of sexual behavior in a way that will be acceptable to everyone is an impossible task, since today there are varying views on the original intent and purpose of human sexuality.

Only the Bible gives us a comprehensive answer. Since we live in a day of moral relativism, since right and wrong no longer have fixed starting and ending points, our children's innocence is continually being attacked.

B. The Attack

Every single day, children are being exposed to information they can't handle:

1. ________________,

2. ________________, and

3. ________________. They are being bombarded by sex-saturated messages, creating curiosity beyond their comprehension and emotional maturity, and by explicit sexual material that overwhelms their moral defenses.

The onslaught of these explicit messages comes long before our children have developed the moral capacity to judge the information ____________.

IV. The Solution

Notes

We believe:

A. Sex education is primarily the responsibility of ________________.

No one can do the job better than properly trained parents, for they are the only ones who have the right to determine what value system is placed into the hearts of their children.

If a child is lacking needed information regarding his sexuality, then the role of a local institution should be equipping parents for the task, not taking over the task by introducing comprehensive sex education curriculums in our schools. That system has failed.

A Harris survey conducted for Planned Parenthood back in 1987 (covering a ten-year period) demonstrated that with virtually unlimited federal tax dollars, school-based comprehensive sex education curriculum saw teen pregnancy double and teen abortions rise 300%.

The belief that comprehensive sex education curriculums do not encourage teen promiscuity was also shattered by the survey. Girls who had no exposure to school-based sex education programs had the lowest rate of pregnancy. Those who had the most exposure had the highest pregnancy rates. In fact, the more money spent, the higher the pregnancy and abortion rates.

California led the packs. In this state we spent 227% more money than the national average per capita, and

Notes

we ended up with a pregnancy rate 133% higher than any state. States that spent the least had the lowest teen pregnancy and abortion rates (McDowell, Josh. The Myth of Sex Education, Here's Life Publication, Inc., 1990).

B. Five Benefits of Training Parents

1. It is more _________ effective.

2. It puts _________________ back on the parents where it belongs.

3. It reduces moral ___________ in the family structure since the value system of the family is not violated by a secular interest.

4. It avoids forcing the institutional _____________ on family and child, such as that in Project 10 (pro-homosexual curriculum).

5. It can be done under the ____________________ conditions since parents pick the time and place rather than resorting to a group classroom setting.

V. Summary

Parents are the rightful audience for this information, for they are the only ones who have the right to determine what value system is placed into the hearts of their children. Advocates of Planned Parenthood and other similar programs say they are interested in protecting children, but their protection is different than ours.

We want to protect our children from __________ intrusion; they want to protect children by moral intrusion.

Notes

Session Two

The Importance of Parental Purity

I. Introduction

Our goal in this session is to look at the biblical record relating to the moral attitudes of Adam, Eve, and God before and after sin entered the world. Much can be derived from looking at how both God and man responded to the change brought on by sin, how God dealt with Adam and Eve's new awareness of their fallen condition, and how they dealt with it.

A. Importance of the Biblical Record

1. It gives us __________ view on the subject.

2. The biblical record tells us that man is unique in the universe (Gen.1:26).

3. Contemporary views speak of animal sexuality, not human sexuality.

4. The biblical record tells us not only what God thinks, but what He _______________.

B. The Questions

1. What was the state of mind of Adam and Eve regarding their bodies before the fall?

Notes

Notes

2. When was the emotion of shame first introduced into humanity?

3. Why didn't God just leave them in their nakedness and tell them it was all right?

4. Where do we draw the line on nudity as it relates to ourselves, our mates, and our children?

5. Is there such a thing as sexual shame? What effects can depravity have on sexual shame?
   To answer these questions we will return to the book of beginnings, the book of Genesis. It is Genesis 2 that establishes the reason for parental purity.

C. The Importance of Parental Purity

1. Parental purity, in and of itself, is a strong influence on a child's moral development because it sets the parameters_______________ and non-acceptable thinking for the child and his sexuality.

2. Parental purity communicates family ____________, which ultimately provide the frame of reference into which your child's moral-sexual perspectives will be fitted.

   How did man's view of sexuality change after he sinned and what was God's response?

II. Genesis 2:22-25

"And the Lord God fashioned into a woman the rib which He had taken from the man, and brought her to the man. And the man said, 'This is now bone of my bones, and flesh of my flesh; she shall be called woman, because she was taken out of man.' For this cause a man shall leave his father and his mother, and shall cleave to his wife; and they shall become one flesh. And the man and his wife were both naked and were not ashamed."

This familiar passage brings into perspective the unity of marriage. The crown of creation was the holy union of the man and woman. This union was of a totally different nature than that of parent and child.

A. With the husband and wife relationship, there is to be a ____________ of the natures.

B. With the parent-child relationship there is a _________ of the child's nature for the future event of blending with a life-long partner in marriage from which children will come, and the cycle is repeated again.

   The essence of the parent/child relationship can never be compared to that of the husband-wife relationship.

C. Two moral statements are made regarding both the man and the woman.

   1. One significant statement reads:, "They were both ______________."

   2. The second is that neither one of them experienced any sense of ____________ in their naked

      There was no sin at that point, no fallen natures, no moral impurities, no evil thoughts, and no corrupt

Notes

Notes

thinking. They were literally in a state of moral perfection, and in that state their nakedness had no corrupt and immoral associations attached to it.

3. There was no shame attached because there was no __________ attached to their condition. The phrase "they were not ashamed" modifies both their physical nakedness and their moral innocence.

D. "Ashamed" and "Nakedness"

1. Ashamed does not mean to be ____________.

2. Ashamed as used in this text is associated with ____________.

   The word nakedness as used in this passage represents more than a general exposure of the body.

3. Specifically, "nakedness" refers to the exposure of the male or female sex organs, a ______________ exposure.

   a. Genesis 9:22-23

   In Genesis. 9:22-23, we read that Ham, the father of Canaan, saw the nakedness of his father. And Shem and Japheth "took a garment and laid it upon both their shoulders and walked backward and covered the nakedness of their father and their faces were turned away, so that they did not see their father's nakedness."

   b. Lam. 1:8

The word is often used of female nakedness, the uncovered sex organs, and is symbolical of shame. In Lam. 1:8, the plundered, devastated Jerusalem is pictured as a woman whose nakedness is exposed, or whose dignity is robbed.

"To uncover one's nakedness" is a frequent euphemism for unacceptable cohabitation and physical relationships.

c. Lev. 18:6

"None of you shall approach any that is near of kin to him, to uncover their nakedness or to have relations with him."

III. Genesis 3:7

"Then the eyes of both of them were opened, and they knew that they were naked; and they sewed fig leaves together and made themselves loin coverings."

The act of sin on the part of Adam and Eve now manifests itself outwardly and there was an immediate effect of this sin upon them both.

A. The first noticeable effect was the awareness of their ______________.

Both are equally guilty, and both experience the same results. They had lost the blessed blindness, the ignorance of innocence, which knows nothing of the shame of nakedness.

B. The very discovery of their nakedness excited shame, which they sought to conceal by an ____________

Notes

Notes

covering. "They sewed fig leaves together and made themselves loin coverings" (Genesis 2:7b).

IV. Genesis 3:8-10

"And they heard the sound of the Lord God walking in the garden in the cool of the day, and the man and his wife hid themselves from the presence of the Lord God among the trees of the garden" (Genesis 3:8).

A. Here we find the influence of sin in man's conscience. It was after man's relationship was broken off because of his disobedience that a consciousness of being naked first compelled a need for ____________. God did not tell them that their original condition changed; they knew it.

   Prior to man's fall, his body of flesh was a perfect dwelling place of his spirit. But sin destroyed the original relationship between the two. Now corruptible emotions joined with a corruptible body to produce a corruptible humanity.

   So as the man and woman stood in each other's presence, they experienced a new emotion – shame.

B. They endeavored to hide the disgrace of their nakedness by covering up parts of their body with ______________.

C. There were no other members of the human race around them that could be ____________ for the emotion of shame. There were no social morés established, no social stereotyping, and no social/religious influence.

   The emotion of shame was there from the moment of

the first act of disobedience on the part of Adam and Eve.

D. The natural feeling of shame associated with our nakedness, the origin of which is recorded in these few verses, did not have its roots in sensuality or any physical corruption, but in the consciousness of __________ before God.
   Consequently, it was the conscience that was really at work, as is evident from the fact that the man and his wife hid themselves from God as soon as they heard the sound of His footsteps.

V. Genesis 3:9-12:

"Then the Lord God called to the man, and said to him, 'Where are you?' And he said, 'I heard the sound of Thee in the garden, and I was afraid because I was naked; so I hid myself.' And He said, 'Who told you that you were naked? Have you eaten from the tree of which I commanded you not to eat?' "

VI. Genesis 3:21

"And the Lord God made garments of skin for Adam and his wife, and clothed them."

The actions of God in this verse are quite significant.

A. From the sacrifice of an innocent animal, man's first clothing was the ___________ of God. By clothing the man and woman, God imparted to them a visible sign of an awakened consciousness of shame and guilt.

   Our nakedness induces shame, and shame is the

Notes

Notes

reminder of guilt. The shamefulness of our nakedness finds its origin in the Fall of man. It is associated with the guilt of sin, and it is passed on to each new baby where it rests within his personhood.

B. Our shame is a reminder of our fallen condition. Shame first came after the Fall of man, and it was God himself who covered man with clothing rather than leave him in his nakedness and thus his shame.

Our society is willing to do anything to flee from the sense of guilt and impending judgement. The open perverse sexual conduct that is prevalent in our society is not only motivated from defiance toward God but out of fear of God. Man today is hiding just as Adam hid after his sin. The only difference is the hiding place.

How does this affect us today as well as affect what we're saying in this series?

VII. Nakedness and Purity

There are basically only three occasions in which nakedness between people of the opposite sex is acceptable.

A. ________________ Setting

B. In ________________

C. Between Parent and ________________

You are the guardian of their bodies and more importantly the guardian of their minds. For the last reason, a child should not have occasion to observe the parents' nakedness. Why? Two reasons.

1. Trespassing ______________ dominion

   The concept of marital dominion is established in 1 Cor. 7:1-5. Your body belongs to your spouse, not your children. There is nothing gained by them seeing you without clothes. And certainly you are not possessing your body in sanctification and honor when you expose yourself to your children. Parental exposure is not an acceptable form of sex education.

2. A child's ____________ nature

   The complexity of human sexuality is forced on the child through the senses long before the mind and heart are prepared to rightly deal with the developing emotions.

VIII. Summary

A. Nakedness is not just biological but is also spiritual.

B. After the Fall, man had a heightened awareness of his own nakedness. The guilt associated with disobedience released the emotion of shame.

C. God acknowledged this by covering man with clothes.

D. There are those who would support and encourage a child in freedom to discover self or encourage nudity as a "natural thing." But these views argue directly against biblical modesty.

E. Modesty (or the lack of it) in a young child has a measurable influence on a child's development.

Notes

Session Three

Marital Intimacy and Marriage Bed Defilers

I. Introduction and Review

II. Marital Intimacy

A. Blending of Natures

"And God created man in His own image, in the image of God He created him; male and female did He create them" (Genesis 1:27).

B. Not Good to Be Alone

"Then the Lord God said, it is not good for man to be alone; I will make him a helper suitable for him" (Genesis 2:18).

1. Alone

2. "Not good to be alone" refers to:

a. ____________________

b. ____________________

Notes

Notes

c. ________________

d. ________________

C. Intimacy

The word "intimacy" comes from the Latin word *intimus* and means the ________________.

Intimacy speaks of emotional closeness between two people and refers to the portion of a relationship that is most private and personal. Intimacy involves the blending of two persons into oneness and sameness.

Statement One

When a husband and wife are not one with each other in regard to emotional, physical, social, and companion oneness, they are alone in that part of their life that is ____________. When that happens, you fail to have total harmony and total intimacy. The act of coming together as one is reduced to fractured parts coming together only to make up a fractured whole. A couple cannot separate physical intimacy from the rest of their ____________.

Statement Two

God is the author of the one-flesh relationship. Marital intimacy is rooted in the security of belonging, being complete, and feeling needed as a completer. God has so designed the inner person that we cannot be truly ____________ with just the physical side of sex.

Notes

III. Marriage Bed Defilers

Marital intimacy is worth protecting, and the crown of intimacy, the marriage bed, should be protected. Hebrews 13:4a tells us that, "Marriage is honorable among all, and the bed undefiled."

A. Marriage Bed Defilers

1. Ignorance that lovemaking is more than ________.

   a. Men who rate lovemaking with their wives as outstanding say that they get much more out of the encounter because of the heightened pleasure they receive from seeing their wives excited and thrilled. This matches up to the provider/protector side of man's nature.

   b. Men need to realize that women respond based upon the signals men give the women (not just in that moment but all day long). She equally finds pleasure in being her husband's completer both in the home and in his heart.

2. ________________ is a hindrance to intimacy and relationships.

   a. It keeps one or both partners away from the sheets of passion.

   b. Mental pictures that are stimulated by passionate scenes on television that cannot be matched in marriage.

3. When one partner is participating and the other is a ____________ rather than a player.

Notes

Because intimacy is a mutual experience of sharing, it is difficult to enter into the enjoyment of it when you are self-absorbed. Shifting your focus to pleasing your partner and enjoying the way your partner pleases you will build intimacy and do away with preoccupation with other things.

4. Lack of ________________.

   We need to read our partner's signals clearly. Inappropriate comments during the act linger afterward. Intimacy develops into complete harmony of love when we are sensitive to our partner's needs, and when we read his or her signals.

   Inappropriate statements linger beyond just one session and stay with your mate in a form of wondering. What do you really think of me, if during this most private time, your focus is on the kids?

5. De-emphasizing the ______________ of sex.

IV. Summary

For the Christian couple, marital intimacy always has a spiritual dimension associated. Unity with a beloved is experienced as two reach the highest possible degree of closeness in heart, soul, mind, and body. For this couple there is no sadness after the act of marriage, but two hearts beating as one with the fullness true intimacy brings. How intimate are you? If you can measure that question in light of God's original intent, you may have a true indicator of how spiritual you are. And all of that takes you one step closer to understanding the big picture so you can pass it on to your children.

Session Four

Cultivating Healthy Attitudes (Part 1)

I. Introduction and Review

A. The challenge of sexual control boils down to whether we will ________________ our sexual impulses or our sexual impulses __________________ us.

B. Two sides of sex education

1. _____________ side

2. _____________ side

C. Statement One

A child's growing curiosity demands that he know the facts, and if he doesn't learn them at home, he will learn them elsewhere under less desirable circumstances. At the same time, the child needs to know how to put the facts into proper perspective within the parameters of human relationships.

A child cannot become master over his biological passions without understanding the moral dynamics involved and becoming a master of those dynamics.

Notes

Notes

II. Three Views of the Body

A. Platonic Dualism

The body is ____________, the soul is ______________, and the two war against each other.

B. Glorified Body

The body is glorified to the point of ______________. Physical health and shape are the ultimate goals.

C. Biblical Perspective

The body is neither ____________ nor ____________ but can be used for both.

Children need to be taught to respect and take care of their bodies. So in the process of communicating the facts of life to your children, a right view of the body must be in place.

III. Influences on Your Child's Attitude

A. Sense of Privacy

B. Nudity and Children

Some parents believe a child is best served when Mom and Dad display their bodies to their children. This is often done by parents taking showers with their children, especially those of the opposite sex, or dressing together. But the practice is more confusing to the child than enlightening. Seeing grown-ups of the opposite sex naked often produces sexual anxiety and frustration with which the child cannot cope. It creates premature feelings that the child is not ready to handle.

C. Gender Differences

"God created him; male and female He created them" (Genesis 1:27).

Men and women have a trail of masculine and feminine adjectives. The two sexes each possess separate and distinct ______________.

Societal sex roles are important. They must remain compatible with the underlying masculine and feminine propensities. God's commands for men and women are most compatible with the manner in which He created them.

1. The Genetic Message

XX = Female

XY = Male

If the father's genetic message of X combines with the mother's X, the gender is female. If the father's genetic message of Y combines with the mother's X, the gender is male.

From the point of conception up to the first six weeks, although genetically and biologically a male or female, in actuality the child only possesses the "nature of a female."

It is not until the 7th week after conception that

Notes

Notes

a genetic message will begin to instruct the developing embryonic sexual organs to develop into masculine or feminine patterns, depending on the original message of XX or XY.

2. Hormonal Message

Just weeks after conception, the embryo or baby is nudged toward masculinity or femininity by a slight but distinct hormonal message.

As the female baby develops, the sex organs, especially the ovaries, begin producing estrogen and progesterone. These are the hormones that facilitate feminine propensities. Since the nature of the baby is female, the child continues to develop with all feminine traits.

But if the original genetic message is XY (male), something altogether different happens in the seventh week. The male sex organs develop and produce hormones, testosterone being the strongest. It is during the seventh week after conception that the hormones enter the blood vessels and are carried through the bloodstream up to the central nervous system, where they begin to act on the brain. The male hormones are literally bringing the brain a message, simply stated: "This is a male; alter brain development to reflect masculine tendencies."

IV. Summary

Statement One

Where does this data takes us? Train your little boys and girls in their natural propensities. When doing so, you are simply encouraging the underlying biological predispositions.

Statement Two

Why is it important to understand the two natures? What are the implications? Every element of man's nature complements every element of the woman's nature perfectly, and the reverse is equally true. Neither Adam nor Eve could represent God's character alone. It is the cleaving together, both spiritually and physically, that represents the totality of God. In your role as Mom and Dad, God's character is best represented by the two of you. Motherhood is not an entity unto itself, neither is fatherhood.

Notes

Session Five

Cultivating Healthy Attitudes (Part 2)

Notes

I. Introduction and Review

In this session we are going to pick up where we left when we began dealing with seven critical concerns influencing healthy and unhealthy attitudes about your children's bodies and their minds.

We have already talked about:
- developing a sense of privacy,
- nudity and children, and
- gender differences.

In this session we will talk about:
- children and sex play,
- bad language,
- the influence of pornography, and
- self-sexual stimulation.

II. Children and Sex Play

It is not uncommon for children between the ages of four and nine to participate in play that is plainly sexual in nature.

There are two basic reasons why children do so. Neither is necessarily right, but the first is more legitimate than the second.

Notes

A. To satisfy their ______________ about the opposite sex.

Think of what is going through the mind of your child when he or she entertains these curious thoughts. What should be going through his mind is Mom or Dad's voice, a recurring loving whisper that "your private body parts are not to be seen by anyone else but Mommy or Daddy now, and in the future your husband or your wife." These are echoes that should be sounded from the earliest years.

So when your child's curiosity leads him to sex play, or when someone else overpowers your child to participate in it, what will go through his or her mind? We hope it is your voice that God is using to bring your children to truth, self-control, and to remind them of error.

B. The child is over-______________ and seeks to act out his premature feelings.

The excessive sexual stimulation found in advertising, television, and magazines places the American youngster in a vulnerable position. Sex play resulting from this kind of stimulation only frustrates the problem even more. Be on guard when it comes to this area of moral preparation. As a parent, do not be the cause of the problem; be the solution.

III. Bad Language

A. Expect it to ______________.

Many times children do not know what they are saying

but think they do. When a child uses a word or concept that is morally offensive or inappropriate, parents need to respond and their response will vary.

B. Parental Responses will vary according to:

1. the ____________ used,

2. the ____________ of the child, and

3. the ____________ for its use.

IV. The Influence of Pornography

Every single day young children are exposed to information they cannot handle emotionally, morally, or spiritually. They are bombarded by sex-saturated messages, creating curiosity beyond their comprehension and emotional maturity. Such information overwhelms their moral defenses.

Please note: There is a direct correlation between exposure and ________.

Pornography Defined: Pornography can be defined as any obscene, immodest written or pictorial material that is deliberately designed to feed perverted sexual desires.

The problem for our children today is that such obscene and lewd material is easily accessible and thus the chance of our children coming in contact with some form of pornography, accidentally or deliberately, is fairly probable.

We would hope that for most of you pornographic material is not likely to enter your home via a magazine or video. But it will come in by way of the television.

Notes

Notes

Monitor what your children are watching, not just the programs but the commercials between the programs. If adult commercials are running, then the program your child is watching is probably not a child's program. The same is true with the radio. What are your kids listening to? Is it something that is reinforcing your family value system or slowly detracting from it?

Once the evil imagination of children is activated, then stimulated, it is hard to get rid of the images stored in the warehouse of their corruptible minds.

V. Self-Sexual Stimulation

There is not a whole lot that really needs to be said that is not already commonly known. Scripture does not directly condone or condemn such a practice. In fact, there are no specific references to self-stimulation in Scripture.

Does that mean we can do what we want? Certainly not! In Matthew 5:28, Jesus said, "But I say to you that whoever looks at a woman to lust for her has already committed adultery with her in his heart."

The precept: Sin is not only located in our ____________ but also in our ____________ process.

A. What do we know about self-stimulation?

B. The Concern

Session Six

Moral Imaginations

I. Introduction and Review

Sex education would be much easier if the only thing parents needed to do is live morally and sexually pure lives in front of their children and not have to answer any questions. But there are questions of curiosity that come up from time to time and those questions need answers. You need to properly direct your child's mind.

But how, when, where, and how much do you tell them, and how much is too much?

II. Guidelines for Answering Questions

A. Principle One: Consider your child's __________.

Consider the child's moral and physical age. Many parents forget this simple principle and thus forget who they are talking to. For example, when a ten-year-old asks, "How did the baby get in your tummy?", that is not the same question as if it had come from a three-year-old. The reason is because the moral maturity levels are different. Attached to the ten-year-old's questions are numerous experiences, associations, and observations. The three-year-old would not have the same experiences.

Notes

Notes

B. Instruction is based on a child's __________ to know and __________ to understand.

When a three-year-old asks, "How did the baby get into your tummy Mommy?", you do not have to get graphic. Test the waters. How much does the child need to know? What is the age of the child? For a three-year-old, the statement, "God put the baby there," is all the child needs to know.

If a five-year-old sister asks about her baby brother, "Mom, what is that thing and why don't I have one?" Give the child the biological information she needs based on God's design for the body. "Because he is a boy and you're a girl and God made boys and girls different." If the question is asked, "What is it used for?" You would answer, "So he can go pee pee." A five-year-old daughter does not need to know any other function than that one.

C. Understand the real ______________ being asked.

Unfortunately parents often answer the wrong question and thereby create more questions in the child's mind.

D. Be careful of descriptive ______________.

When communicating biological facts to your children, what terminology should be used? This is where parents go to extremes.

1. The extremes
   a.

   b.

2. Biblical terminology

   We do not believe it is helpful to make up new terminology but we also believe it is far from healthy to explain to very young children the facts of life in adult terminology. The Bible talks of many body parts and calls them by their exact names, except for the genitals, which are either spoken of in poetic language or referred to as nakedness. That is the only part of our bodies that God refers to in general and distant terms. The leg in scripture is a leg. The arm is an arm, the neck is a neck, the bowel is the bowel, a toe is a toe, but the genitals are referred to as nakedness, or fountains or springs.

   Your children will learn the medical terminology as they grow older, and as they are able to process such adult terms. For now the use of innocent and mutually and socially accepted terminology for body parts is fine. Using words such as "hiney," or "bottom," or "pee pee," or "little bum," are appropriate. You are conveying, in culturally accepted terminology, morally non-offensive titles to your children's body parts.

   Some say, "Don't make a big deal out of it; after all parts are parts. There is no difference between an arm, a leg or the genitals. Parts are parts." The problem with this assumption is that the arm is not an object of sexual attraction or fantasy. The leg is not connected to the act of sex, there is nothing sexually appealing about a toe. But when exact and descriptive titles are given to the genitals, sexual thoughts and sensations are put on alert even in children. Sex, not urination, becomes the object of thought.

Notes

Notes

That is why the use of innocent, general terms will help preserve the child's developing moral value system because general terms do not force the child into such narrow, restrictive categories of thinking or sexual thoughts that exact terminology fosters.

That is why morally protecting a child from being offended and being offensive is every parent's responsibility. General terms help you communicate what you want to say without pinpointing the purpose or function of the organ. When we say to our children, "Cover up your little hiney," it means cover up your entire little bottom.

The bottom line is this: We are not just animals, and we exist in more than just the flesh. We are moral creatures. You cannot talk about the plumbing side of sex education without giving due consideration to the moral implications of such conversation, even with young children. And until your child is able to handle the moral implication of your verbiage, it is best to stay away from any word usage that pushes him ahead of his moral capabilities.

III. The Problem of Evil Imaginations

When we speak of the imagination, we do so from both a theological and developmental perspective. The imagination is part of our thinking process and works not from abstract thought but from concrete input via the senses. Sight and hearing are the two most open channels that feed the imagination. The imagination is very sensitive to sexual issues.

In an earlier session we talked of a twelve-year-old San Francisco boy whose mind became polluted with dial-a-porn sex messages. Sexual images were conveyed to him, stored in his imagination, and at the right time, when opportunity was present, he channeled these images to action and sexually assaulted an innocent four-year-old girl. If the words and images were not stored in his imagination, the assault would not have taken place.

A. The Biblical Record

Genesis 6:5 – 8:21
Jeremiah 3:17 (Heart)
Romans 1:21 (Heart)

Definition:

1. Imagination is the power to select parts of different concepts or objects of _______________ to form a whole more pleasing, more terrible, or more awful image than has ever been presented in the ordinary course of nature.

2. Memory is the faculty of the mind by which it retains knowledge of past events or ideas.

B. The imagination has the ability to process both ______________ and ______________thoughts.

C. The power of the human imagination

1. It has the power to form mental images of what is not actually ____________.

2. It has the power to create mental images of what has never been actually ________________ before.

3. It has the power to create new images or ideas by

Notes

Notes

combining previous _______________.

Here is an example of how the imagination can gather image data, store and recall it. The first illustration is non-moral. In this exercise, you will experience the following:

1. Form a mental image of what is not actually _______________.

2. Create an image of something that has never been _____________, and

3. Create a new image by combining _____________ experiences.

4. Questions:

   a. How many of you have ever seen traffic back up both ways on the Golden Gate Bridge? It is possible, but what you created in your minds was an image of something that is not present.

   b. How many of you have ever seen a man stand on a bridge flipping a fried egg with a crowd of people around him applauding his performance? Probably none of you. Not that such a scene is not possible. But you created an image of something you have not seen or experienced.

   c. How many of you have seen an egg scoot across the road, hold its nose, jump from the bridge, be saved by a parachute, and then eaten by a sea gull?

IV. How Does it Work?

The words we used were already in your memory. We took those words from your memory, arranged them, and made a picture in your mind. And the more the story is repeated, or the more the simulator words are brought to our attention (simulators being the flipping of the egg, the clapping of the crowd, the egg scooting with six legs across the pavement, the parachute opening, etc.), the deeper embedded the imagery becomes.

But if you never hear the story again, the memory of it will fade. By this time next month, you might forget the story and the imagery associated with it, and the reason for that is: The imagination is stimulated by one of three activities.

A. Three ways the imagination is stimulated

1. ________________

2. ________________

3. ________________ arousement and curiosity

In the story we shared with you, although there was action, the words and the scenes described were not tied to emotions or sexual arousement. It was a morally neutral story, and thus one that could quickly fade in your imagination.

But what if the story had sexual associations tied to its character? What if what I had described had sexual actions tied to it? What if the story aroused feelings of curiosity and feelings for sexual exploration? How long would it stay in the imagination and how many times would the scenes be replayed in your mind?

Notes

Notes

May we suggest that for most people, it would linger longer, and the scene would be played many more times because it appeals to our base nature.

The Question

How do you prevent your child's friends from polluting what you put into your child? How do you police your child's imagination when his peers betray your teaching by sharing and suggesting sexual activities?

B. The Old Man and the Stage Coach

Story from audio/video

C. Statements

When communicating sexual information to a child, information that the child is not morally ready to filter or process, the words that have strong and active images attached to them are stored in memory, ready to be used by the imagination. But passive words, such as hiney, bum, or pee pee are weak and nondescript and do not force imagery, nor are they used by society to paint sexual pictures in the mind.

The problem is not the directness of the approach or the terms themselves, but rather the inability of parents to control the moral climate and influences outside of their homes from which wrongful associations are made. would be played many more times because it appeals to our base nature.

Session Seven

The Indirect Method of Sex Education

I. Introduction and Review

II. Direct Versus Indirect Methods

A. Direct Method

B. Problems with the Direct Method

1. It violates the progressive laws of ____________.

2. Children cannot morally handle the ____________ presented. Their senses are overwhelmed.

3. The direct method wrongly feeds a child's imagination.

C. The Indirect Approach

Statement One

This is the best way and the first step to communicating the facts of life to your children. It will allow you to teach them everything they need to know without giving them too much or too little information. And

Notes

Notes

it is done without embarrassment or shame or the withholding of facts.

Statement Two

With the indirect approach you do not wait until the child asks questions. The younger the child the better. With the direct approach, the younger the child, the more damaging.

D. Indirect Defined

Statement

Indirect means all learning comes by way of taking knowledge gained through a morally ______________ object and then helping the child transfer that knowledge to himself, as he needs it.

E. The Morally Neutral Fact File

As a parent, you will create a morally innocent mental file in your child's mind that will be stored in memory. Your child will have access to the file any time he wants. What is placed in the file is a morally neutral example that communicates the facts of life. Because it's morally neutral and because there are no __________, __________ or __________ feelings associated, the file is stored in memory, safely kept away from the imagination. Periodically, you will add more information to the file to keep it updated.

1. The child will only ______________ from the file what he needs and can handle mentally, emotionally, and morally.

2. There is nothing ______________ in the file.

3. There is nothing that will ______________ the moral imaginations of the child.

4. There is nothing that will ______________ the moral innocence of the child.

5. Everything is there to help the child understand the basic ______________ about human sexuality.

III. The Birds and The Bees

Have you ever wondered why, in a manner of jest, parents often refer to sex education in association with the birds and the bees? People use to ask, "Have you talked with your children about the birds and the bees?"

Therein lies the answer. There is a history to the statement. It is more than a cute phrase. That statement carried a coded message that adults understood.

A. What do birds and the bees have in common? The ______________.

B. What is the morally neutral object?

Historically, sex education was communicated through objects of nature such as puppies, kittens, and baby lambs being born.

The most morally neutral and yet biologically comprehensive example to use when communicating biological realities to children is the ______________.

Notes

Notes

C. The Explanation

For young children, the most basic questions of life are answered by the natural analogy that can be drawn from the flower. When you use the flower, the story of reproductive life is told without using any sexual imagery. The flower itself becomes the morally neutral object that you as parents can keep going back to as your child grows older and as his or her questions become more and more involved. Because the object is the flower, and not mommy or daddy or the child's private body parts, no embarrassment is induced nor is there the need to overindulge your child in descriptive terminology that can be acted upon by a peer who represents to your child a different moral value system than what you have in your home.

D. The Three Stages of Communication

1. The ________________ stage

2. The ________________ stage

3. The ________________ stage

E. The Information Stage

The Walk

As you take a walk with your child, speak to him of God's creative work and how He made all things beautiful. Here is a sample conversation:

"God made all things beautiful, and He made at least two of everything: fish, birds, cats, dogs, and people.

Adam and Eve had children and their children had more children and in time the whole world was filled up with people. The whole world is also filled up with flowers.

God made this flower in such a way that it can actually have baby flowers (which come from seeds), and they get planted and grow up and have baby flowers. Here, I'm going to show you just how God did this wonderful thing. (See figure 1 and notes.)

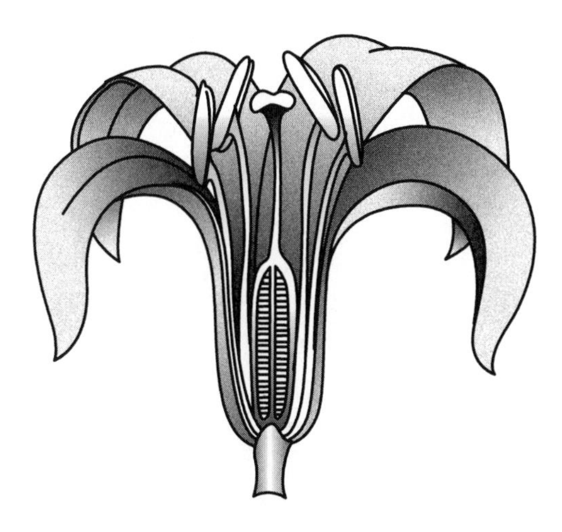

Figure7-1

(The drawing above shows a flower cut open down one side. You can see the four stamen, each with a stem leading to the pollen sacs (anthers). This is the male portion of the flower. Also note the female center stem which is called the pistil. The pistil receives the pollen grain to begin the process of fertilization. (For more detailed information, please see any encyclopedia.)

Do you see the stem coming out of the top of the flower? That is like the daddy part of the flower. These little dust particles are called pollen, seeds that the daddy part produces. Way down in here, it looks like

Notes

Notes

a vase; this is the mommy part of the flower. Inside the mommy part of the flower, there is a tiny egg. When this flower grows up, the tiny pollen seeds drop way down inside and touch the mommy part. When the seed and the egg touches, they join together and form a baby flower. The baby flower (the seed) stays in the mother part until it grows sufficiently to come out and grows to be a flower by itself."

F. The Curious Stage

The Questions

This stage begins when the child asks, "Why is the baby in your tummy?"

First, review the flower again. By now, you will add more information. For example, you may say, "Remember when the daddy seed that comes from the pollen comes in contact with the mommy part of the flower and touches the tiny egg? That egg actually comes from a part of the flower called the ovaries. Just like the flower has two ovaries, mommy has ovaries, too. That's where the egg comes from.

After the pollen seed and the egg touch and become a baby seed, it needs to grow in a safe place, and it grows in a little womb inside the mommy part of the flower. And just like the baby flower grows inside the mommy part of the flower, you grew inside mommy's womb until you were ready to be born."

"But mommy, how does the baby get out once it gets in there?"

(Go back to the flower.)

"When the flower baby is ready to come out of the little womb, God causes it to be gently pushed out, where it falls to the ground and grows into a new flower. The same thing happens with a human baby, except it doesn't fall on the ground. When the baby is ready to come out, mommy's body starts to push the baby out from where it's growing."

"Mommy, where is that opening?"

"Because God created mommies to carry babies, He also created a special place for the babies to come out. It's right next to where your pee pee comes out."

G. The Comparative Stage

This stage is usually a reactive, indirect response that you are going to give and not a proactive response. It usually is the response to a question such as: "How did the baby get into your tummy?"

Go back to the flower. By this age, the child may have seen kittens, puppies, bunnies, or baby lambs being born, which may allow you to add to your explanation by using other objects of nature as well as the flower.

Speaking to the child, remind him or her of the boy part of the flower and the pollen seed that it makes and how the pollen travels down to the girl part of the flower to meet the egg that comes from the ovaries. Then explain:

"In the flower, God made the male and female parts within each flower. But with human beings, God made a daddy and a mommy that are not together. Daddy

Notes

Notes

still has a seed in his body and mommy still has the eggs in her body. When a man and a woman love each other and are married, they begin to want to have a baby. God put the seed in a daddy's private body parts. At a special time, a daddy and a mommy lay down close to each other, so close that their private body parts touch, and then a great miracle takes place. The seed that is in a daddy travels from his body over to mommy's body. And just like the flower, the mommy's body takes the seed, brings it to the egg, and the baby is conceived. That's where you came from. That is when the baby begins to grow inside the womb. It takes nine months for the baby to grow, and then it comes out. And that's how you got here."

IV. Summary

The ages at which you communicate the three stages of information will vary according to each child based upon the moral maturity level of the child, the brothers and sisters, and the social climate around the house. The beauty is that once you lay down the foundation with the flower, you always have a morally neutral point to come back to and a starting point for you to ask them questions to measure their understanding.

As parents, you are continually teaching sexual attitudes. With the flower, you are only teaching biological truth. They go hand in hand and both are necessary to balance off the other. If you fail in either area, you will fail to communicate God's original intent for the use of the body. You cannot teach the biological without the spiritual – the physical without the moral side.

Session Eight

Common Questions

Notes

We provided the following series of questions and answers as a supplement to the first seven session. The questions below represent broad categories of topics of frequently asked topics. For your quick review the questions are listed first followed by our response.

Question Summary

Question #1
We understand that parents' nakedness is inappropriate for our children, but what about a father in his briefs? What do you think about a dad who spends time around the house this way? What about a mate who uses the bathroom with the door open?

Question #2
What are the general guidelines for sibling bathing: both children of the same gender and brothers and sisters bathing together? What about boys and girls sharing a bedroom together or older youths showering together after gym classes?

Question #3
What are the guidelines for parents bathing with their children?

Question #4
What do you do about the beach and what you're likely to see there in terms of bathing suits?

Question #5
When do you discuss self-stimulation with your child, or do you not discuss it at all?

Notes

Question #6
If love is an action and not a feeling, then is lovemaking something you should do even if you do not feel like it? How do you communicate this to your mate without hurting is or her feeling?

Question #7
What if your child's personality is such that he or she does not ask questions because physical things are yucky?

Question #8
Do the XY signals during the seventh and eighth weeks of development support the homosexual premise of a genetic difference?

Question #9
How do parents undo biological information already gained through the school or other public forums? How is this information realigned with the analogy of the flower? How do you handle a situation in which your child brings you a question that is full of polluted material?

Question #10
If a parent had lived a morally loose life before marriage and a commitment to Christ, would an older child benefit from this knowledge to protect them from making the same mistake or would this create more problems? What if your moral innocence was taken from you at a very young age?

Question #11
How do you explain to a young child why a single girl is pregnant? The children know that she is not married, so how do we resolve this conflict in their minds?

Question #12
Where do you start if your kids are too old for you to use the gradual proactive indirect method?

Question #13
How do you address the issue of children who are older and understand the "terms" and uses as a result of being raised around animals on a farm? Is there a need to use other terms?

Question #14
At what age do you talk about the physical changes that take place at puberty?

Question #15
When do you explain sexual slang words? Do you have to explain sexual slang words?

Question #16
When and how do you prepare your son or daughter for the consummation of their wedding night?

Question #17
Today, toy manufacturers are making dolls that are anatomically correct. What are your thoughts on this matter?

Question #18
When reading the Scriptures to your children how do you deal with sensitive passages?

Question #19
How do you explain the question, "Where did I come from?" to an adopted child?

Question #20
As a family we have explained to our children that we discuss body parts or bodily functions in the home with Mom and Dad. The world seems to condone the idea of curiosity, exploration, and discussion of these things. In view of the two extremes, my question is this: Should I intervene and ask my two older children, six and eight, to change the subject when I overhear them discussing bodily differences with their friends?

Notes

Notes

Question #1
We understand that parents' nakedness is inappropriate for our children, but what about a father in his briefs? What do you think about a dad who spends time around the house this way? What about a mate who uses the bathroom with the door open?

Moving quickly from bathroom to bedroom is not a problem. It gets back to attitude. What are you trying to cultivate in the hearts and minds of your children? It is not a healthy thing for a dad or mom to parade around in briefs. It is not so much an attitude that we are trying to suppress but one we are trying to create. Modesty needs to be cultivated in our sons as well as our daughters.

Question #2
What are the general guidelines for sibling bathing: both children of the same gender and brothers and sisters bathing together? What about boys and girls sharing a bedroom together or older youths showering together after gym classes?

For the same gender, around five or six years old is okay for bathing together. You want to watch for when the older sibling begins developing modesty on his own and wants privacy. For the opposite sex, it should be younger. As soon as you see one of the children starting to become curious and doing more than innocent play, that's the time to start separate baths.

There are three positions relating to locker-room showers: ideal, acceptable, and tolerable. Boys' gym showers are acceptable. For girls, it is different. Girls were made by God differently with a more discriminating attitude. Prior to the 1960s and 1970s, girls had separate stall showers because there was a belief system that recognized the predisposition to modesty in women. The push in the 1970s for gang showers was influenced by the movement that girls are not different than boys, so if boys have gang showers, girls should too. This is a situation that you tolerate while you continue to encourage the right attitude in the home.

Question #3
What are the guidelines for parents bathing with their children?

We recommend that bathing with your child should not go beyond the first year. You need to think from the mind of the child: what are they seeing, and how will it affect them as they get older? Again we will say: It is not so much an attitude that we are trying to suppress but one we are trying to create.

Question #4
What do you do about the beach and what you're likely to see there in terms of bathing suits?

One practical thing to do is to look for family spots. These are often indicated by swing sets, etc. You are not going to prevent your children from seeing everything, but you will minimize what they see. Another helpful thing to do when you are at the beach is to sit as close to the water as possible, so you can avoid the parade of people in front of you causing your children to wonder. For bathing suits, it is difficult trying to explain the problem of causing other people to stumble. Start little girls off young wearing modest, one-piece bathing suits.

It's not enough to teach them what to do. Give them the reason why. You need to teach the moral reason why. That is what separates authoritarianism from authoritativeness.

Question #5
When do you discuss self-stimulation with your child, or do you not discuss it at all?

Notes

Notes

The best time for such a conversation is to start early. Young children who touch themselves (eighteen months to three years old) do not do so out of a sexual motivation but because they have found something that is pleasurable. It's at that time that you help them get control. You may make it a discipline problem, but be careful. Do not discipline them for touching themselves. That is not the issue. You discipline them for disobedience (don't touch). When it first starts with a younger child, gently take the child's hand away and say, "Don't touch." We don't want a critical spirit or to beat the child down. You may want to explain that this is not good. There may be something on their fingers that could hurt them or cause an infection. You don't want to scare them. If the problem exists, don't wait until it becomes a compulsive habit to correct it.

Question #6
If love is an action and not a feeling, then is lovemaking something you should do even if you do not feel like it? How do you communicate this to your mate without hurting is or her feeling?

Love is part of a relationship that takes place every moment of the day. It is more than an action. It is also a feeling. Feeling and action are legitimate parts of the equation and both must be respected in the marriage relationship. Saying "no" must be with love, just as asking for a "yes" must be said with love.

Question #7
What if your child's personality is such that he or she does not ask questions because physical things are yucky?

Take the child back to the flower because it allows you to communicate the necessary facts. If a child responds with, "That's yucky," take a clue that he is not ready for more progressive details. Also, if a child continues with, "Tell me more," you have to decide where that child is in his moral maturity and age. He may be morally ready but still too young.

Question #8
Do the XY signals during the seventh and eighth weeks of development support the homosexual premise of a genetic difference?

Notes

There are seven realities to consider.

1. The Bible condemns the practice of homosexuality (1 Cor. 6:9-10).

2. There are no homosexuals just the practice of homosexuality. It is not possible to be a genetic condition since homosexuals cannot reproduce their specie. Nor is it a worldwide phenomenon.

3. There is a higher incidence in societies where the natures of men and women are blended (such as in the American society).

4. Those who practice homosexuality have no desire to be a girl. The practice is rooted in relationships or lack of. It is not rooted in brain function predisposition. Many very masculine men practice homosexuality.

5. The common thread through history for those who practice homosexuality is the absence of a father figure physically and emotionally, and negative feelings toward the father. For men, there is often an over-pampering mother.

6. The homosexual population is less than 2 percent of the population, more likely less than 1 percent.

Question #9
How do parents undo biological information already gained through the school or other public forums? How is this information realigned with the analogy of the flower? How do you

Notes

handle a situation in which your child brings you a question that is full of polluted material?

First, parents need to work on the protection and sheltering of children so they won't be polluted. If they already have been, go to the source and find out where they are getting the information and then work on protecting them from that outside stimulation so they are not further damaged. Some of this can come from family members or mates who don't see any problem with showing R-rated movies. Go back to the flower as often as possible so that it is foremost in their minds. You cannot exclude this teaching from all the other things you are teaching. You should be working on a trusting relationship with your children, so that as you are building that relationship and they know they can trust you as Mom or Dad when they hear something that is possibly questionable, they can come and talk to you. Don't focus so much on the moral issue that you neglect the relationship. For parents that used the anatomical names before, don't try to undo it, but continue to build around the child a hedge of purity.

Question #10
If a parent had lived a morally loose life before marriage and a commitment to Christ, would an older child benefit from this knowledge to protect them from making the same mistake or would this create more problems? What if your moral innocence was taken from you at a very young age?

The answer can be found in Psalm 103:12, "As far as the east is from the west, so far has He removed our transgressions from us." If God has removed your transgressions from you, why should you bring them back? Don't rejoice in your iniquity; don't bring it back up. You do not help your children mature morally when you bring up the past, as wretched as that may be. If you want to speak in generalities about your past, that may be fine, but you do not have to go into detail. They do not need to know who was involved. They just need to know you are thankful for the new life you have in Christ because now you understand what life is all about and you are better able to equip your children in their lives. If you are living a morally pure life before them, especially as teenagers, you can share with them that one of your goals for them is to be better Christians than you were. They may have a hard time understanding God's grace in this area.

Question #11
How do you explain to a young child why a single girl is pregnant? The children know that she is not married, so how do we resolve this conflict in their minds?

Depending on the age of the child, you can say that sometimes people who are not married pretend that they are. With a nonjudgmental spirit, tell them that is not God's design. God wants people to be married.

Question #12
Where do you start if your kids are too old for you to use the gradual proactive indirect method?

You start with the flower, even with an older child. For some of you, it may take some rethinking in your own mind to use something neutral. Explain how the flower works, then ask them, "Okay, what have you heard? How do you think this relates?" We are talking roughly around ages ten and older. At least by ten, most kids start to hear things and begin to ask questions.

Question #13
How do you address the issue of children who are older and\ understand the "terms" and uses as a result of being raised around animals on a farm? Is there a need to use other terms?
There is not a need to use other terms. You may want to use the flower illustration. But when you're on the farm, there are so many natural examples that you can use. A chicken laying

Notes

Notes

an egg is a natural example. The baby calf, lamb, or kittens are also good opportunities. Most of you live in the city, and that is why the flower is the best analogy.

Question #14
At what age do you talk about the physical changes that take place at puberty?

When you notice that your daughter begins to develop, it's time to begin discussing the changes that will be taking place in her body. Do not wait until it happens! Sit your daughter down, depending on your own genetic history, between nine to twelve years of age. The flower could be a starting point because it has ovaries and a womb-like nest. This is a time to introduce morally proper terms, such as the womb, ovaries, and egg. For a girl, particularly, you can just say when the baby is born it comes through the birth canal. You don't have to get real descriptive. All will come in time. For fathers and sons, spending a weekend together to discuss these issues is fine if there has been the preparation done (with the flower, etc). If there has been no moral preparation, this can be devastating to a son. Remember, sex education is progressive. With the direct method, the more you tell and the earlier you tell them, the more devastating it is. With the indirect method, the earlier you start with the flower, the better.

(For a complete discussion on communicating the facts of life to pre-adolescents, dads to sons and mothers to daughters, please pick up *On Becoming Preteenwise*, by Gary Ezzo and Dr. Robert Bucknam. Chapters 13 and 14 offer practical steps in how to prepare your sons and daughters for the bodily changes taking place and how to maintain an attitude of purity and dignity.)

Question #15
When do you explain sexual slang words? Do you have to explain sexual slang words?

You don't necessarily have to explain them when children come home with them. You can just say, "Those aren't words that we use in our home." Remember the issue of family identity. You are cultivating family identity. Your children may not even ask some specific things. You may ask your child what he thinks the word means. You don't need to go into a long explanation.

Question #16
When and how do you prepare your son or daughter for the consummation of their wedding night?
All sex education is progressive. Not only are you communicating biological truths, you are communicating attitudes and spiritual truth. By the time your children are ready for marriage, they should have a holy understanding of the husband/wife relationship and the beauty of that relationship. Even though they may not have all of the black-and-white details, they will know, they will be prepared, because their hearts are prepared. If you prepare the heart, the mind will follow.

Question #17
Today, toy manufacturers are making dolls that are anatomically correct. What are your thoughts on this matter?

This is part of the androgenous movement that is trying to show that boys and girls are the same except for body parts. We do not recommend sex education toys like this. We think these toys are wrong and send the wrong message. We believe such thinking runs contrary to Scripture in that it is trying to communicate something that is not true. There are male and female differences, and they are more than just outward sex differences. We personally don't recommend the use of those toys as part of sex education.

Question #18
When reading the Scriptures to your children how do you deal with sensitive passages?

Notes

Notes

As parents, do not try to avoid reading these passages but rather change any word that may not be appropriate given your child's age or moral maturity. For example, in Genesis 34, it says "He took her and lay with her by force." You can change this to "treated her meanly." You are communicating the intent of the passage to your children but are not morally pushing them ahead of their understanding. We suggest you not make the Song of Solomon the topic for family devotions if you have young children.

Question #19
How do you explain the question, "Where did I come from?" to an adopted child?

It isn't any different than any other child asking. If you are using the flower example, then they will have that type of information. By the time a child asks that question, hopefully that child already knows he is adopted and the parents have already been dealing with how he has been chosen and how thankful they are that God has provided him as the child. You will just use the flower as with any other child.

Question #20
As a family we have explained to our children that we discuss body parts or bodily functions in the home with Mom and Dad. The world seems to condone the idea of curiosity, exploration, and discussion of these things. In view of the two extremes, my question is this: Should I intervene and ask my two older children, six and eight, to change the subject when I overhear them discussing bodily differences with their friends?

It is unlikely that young children are appropriately discussing their anatomy. Yes, it is right for you to intervene and simply say, "We don't need to be talking about that."

Question #21

Regarding the flower, do you begin with the information stage and then just wait for the curious and comparative stage to happen?

Yes, for those who have young children. The proactive, indirect approach lets you start by using a neutral object. If you use the proactive indirect approach from the beginning, the reactive stage will come naturally. The information stage will start around three or four years of age. The curious stage may begin around six or seven years of age, and depending on the child, the comparative stage around eight or nine years of age. With these three stages, you may function in a proactive mode or a reactive mode. It all depends on the child, his readiness, and his questions. It depends on whether it's the first child or the fifth child, the child on the farm or in the city. There are other variables that are going to cause the child to bring his curious questions to you. The question is, are you ready and have you established the morally neutral object to start to communicate the facts?

Notes

Appendix

Alfred Kinsey and the Sexual Revolution

by Audrey Werner
Foreword by Anne Marie Ezzo

FOREWARD

It's was called the 'sexual revolution' with free love, free sex and no moral restraints. As we all know, for any revolution to occur there must be someone or a group of people who begin the process of introducing revolutionary ideas into the populace. During the 1950s and 60s, there was a man whose revolutionary ideas shaped the way the Western world would view human sexuality.

As a professor of biology this man believed that human sexuality could be studied much like insects or laboratory animals. Over the course of time he applied for and received large grants from the Rockefeller Foundation to conduct surveys to prove his hypothesis. His name was Alfred Kinsey. His published works of 1948 and 1953 earned him the title as the "Father of the Sexual Revolution". Little did anyone know that he would become one of the greatest influences of social change and moral decline in the twentieth century. His legacy is clearly with us today.

There is much that can be said about Mr. Kinsey, very little that is edifying from a Christian worldview. But if you are at all involved with youth work, children's ministry or education in general, you will benefit from picking up the insightful book, *Kinsey: Crimes and Consequences* by Dr. Judith Reisman. You can also visit RSVP America's website at www.rsvpamerica.org. There you can obtain well documented reports and a history on and about Dr. Kinsey and the foundations of his beliefs. It is worth the visit.

To serve our immediate readership and to provide valuable insights into Dr. Kinsey, his beliefs, research methods and impact on your family today, we invited a far greater authority than ourselves to help us bring this message. Audrey Werner is a registered nurse, founder of The Matthew XVIII Group, a public speaker on women's health issues, and the influence of Kinsey's science on the Church. The Werners are parents of four children and their GFI involvement has been ongoing since the mid 1990s. We are sure you will find Audrey's comments enlightening and helpful.

Anne Marie Ezzo

Alfred Kinsey and the Sexual Revolution

By Audrey Werner R.N.

It's all about the children — our children, your children, the children of the world. It is the duty of every society to protect children from any form of abuse. Yet, no greater assault has come on any youth generation with such speed and destruction as has the influence of Dr. Alfred Kinsey. To understand the far reaching impact of Dr. Kinsey's reports, one only needs to step back in time to the last century. It was in the 1930s when Dr. Kinsey, trained as a zoologist and serving as a biology professor at Indiana University, began to stray from his scientific specialty, the 'Gall' wasp, to his unbridled passion, human sexuality.

Dr. Kinsey believed human sexuality should be studied without regard to moral constraints. That is, all aspects of human sexuality are strictly biological functions void of any related virtue. In his humanistic paradigm, man is the end product of biological chance, void of a soul, spirit, or a redeeming God. Therefore all sex should be seen in light of a biological process, unfettered from morality.

In less than a decade of his published reports he became what Gore Vidal called "the most famous man in the world". His two published studies included, "Sexual Behavior in the Human Male" in 1948 and "Sexual Behavior in the Human Female" in 1953.

Because the Kinsey Reports were initially thought to be authoritative and reliable, his findings brought about revolutionary changes in law, medicine, science, education and Christian ministries in the realm of public sexual conduct according to Dr. Judith Reisman, author of *Kinsey: Crimes and Consequences* (1998, 2000). Even the modern gay rights movement was a direct spin off of Kinsey's writings. The pornography industry of today is a direct result of the Kinsey influence. The graph's on pages 83-84 show corresponding trends in social sexual behavior that came as a consequence of the Kinsey Reports.

UNDER THE LIGHT

In the early 1980's, Dr. Reisman began to look more closely at Dr. Kinsey's revolutionary ideas and "scientific" method. What she uncovered was the lack of full public disclosure of the methods used by Kinsey to collect his data and his fraudulent means to obtain his desired outcomes. Today, it is publicly known that Kinsey hired pedophiles to "experiment" on children. In his own 'Male volume', the reports of nine pedophiles, who manipulated children, were used as part of his authoritative conclusion that children are erotic beings from birth with a desire and capacity for sex. He concluded that where there is a capacity there should be freedom.

Initially the Kinsey Reports were considered impressive because the findings were supposedly based on 18,000 interviews. However, only about a quarter of these were actually processed and used in his two reports. Roughly 86% of the respondents who made it into the Kinsey's "Male" volume were based on sexual deviants and registered sex offenders, including 1,600 sex felons. The Kinsey Reports claimed this group represented the average American male. Those reports that did not match Kinsey's desired outcome were thrown out.

By the 1960's, Kinsey's revolutionary model of human sexuality was a standard part of University level curriculum. By 1964 SIECUS, the (Sex Information and Education Council of the United States), was formed by leaders of the new sexuality meeting at the Kinsey Institute. The primary purpose of SIECUS existence is to teach the Kinsey model of human sexuality, (i.e. anything goes) anywhere and everywhere. SIECUS became the resource center for distributing information including training materials for teachers and health-care professionals, as well as sample curricula for the classroom.

From medical-school classrooms to the kindergarten classrooms, SIECUS published guidelines for Comprehensive Sexuality Education, has infiltrated every nook and cranny of the American society. These guidelines were created by the "National Guideline Task Force" a committee made up of Kinsey's associates and disciples, including Planned Parenthood and the National Lesbian and Gay Health Foundation to name a few.

From 1964 to the present, the Kinsey Institute, Planned Parenthood and SIECUS (all recipients of grants from Playboy Magazine) taught the new standard in America's classrooms. Because teaching sex education is mandated in most states, teachers are trained in the Kinsey model at the university level before entering the classroom to teach our children sex education. Although our society has become much more open in regards to matters of sexuality, most parents today would be shocked to realize the extent of explicit sexual knowledge the Kinsey Institute seeks to provide your children. For example, the "21 Things SIECUS Wants Your Five Year Old to Know" would violate the conscience of most adults. If this is what they propagate for 5-year olds, imagine their list and plans for your preteen and teenagers.

THE KINSEY STATISTICAL LEGACY

In retrospect what have we learned about the moral legacy of the Kinsey Report? Has it been good for America? Good for the world? Has open "sexuality" been positive for individuals, families or society? The charts on page 79 & 80 were assembled by the US Department of Commerce and Census Bureau reveal the legacy of the Kinsey reports.

Where are the Christian voices in all of this? Unfortunately, much of the institutional church was trained in the Kinsey data at colleges and universities that accepted Kinsey as the final authority on sexual conduct – even over the Word of God. The foundations of some very popular and widely used Christian sex education curricula can be traced directly back to SIECUS and the Kinsey model.

How can you know if the Kinsey approach

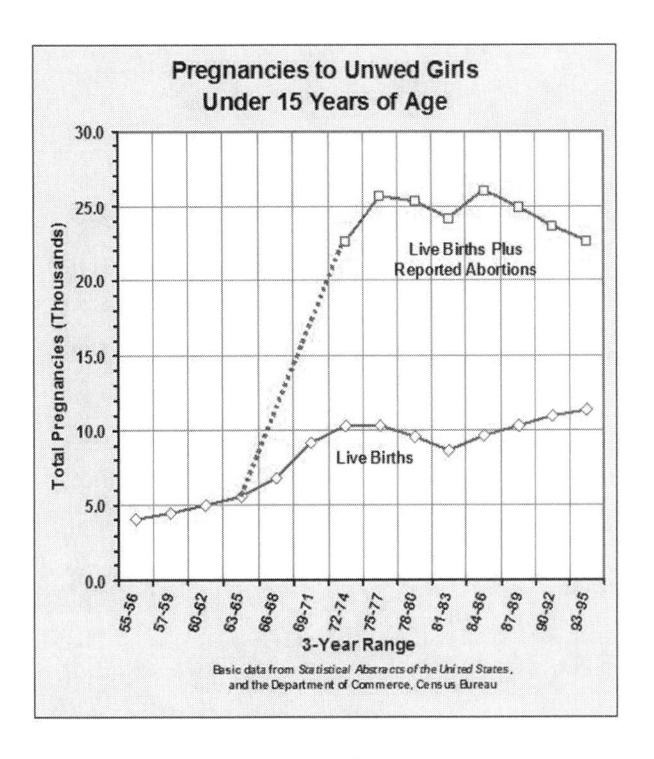
Pregnancies to Unwed Girls
Under 15 Years of Age
Total Pregnancies (Thousands)
30.0
25.0
20.0
15.0
10.0
5.0
0.0
Live Births Plus
Reported Abortions
Live Births
55-56
57-59
60-62
63-65
66-68
69-71
72-74
75-77
78-80
81-83
84-86
87-89
90-92
93-95
3-Year Range
Basic data from Statistical Abstracts of the United States,
and the Department of Commerce, Census Bureau

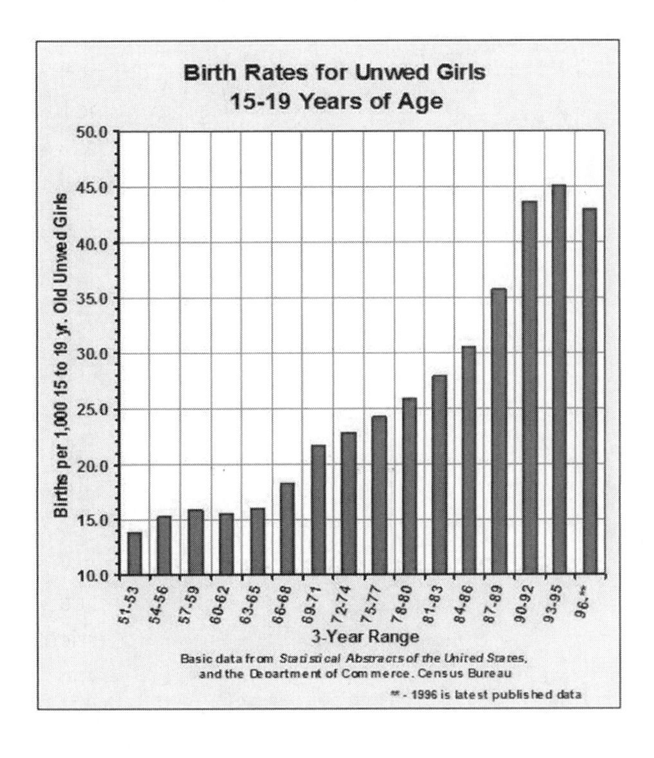
Birth Rates for Unwed Girls
15-19 Years of Age
Births per 1,000 15 to 19 yr. Old Unwed Girls
50.0
45.0
40.0
35.0
30.0
25.0
20.0
15.0
10.0
51-53
54-56
57-59
60-62
63-65
66-68
69-71
72-74
75-77
78-80
81-83
84-86
87-89
90-92
93-95
96-**
3-Year Range
Basic data from Statistical Abstracts of the United States,
and the Department of Commerce, Census Bureau
** - 1996 is latest published data

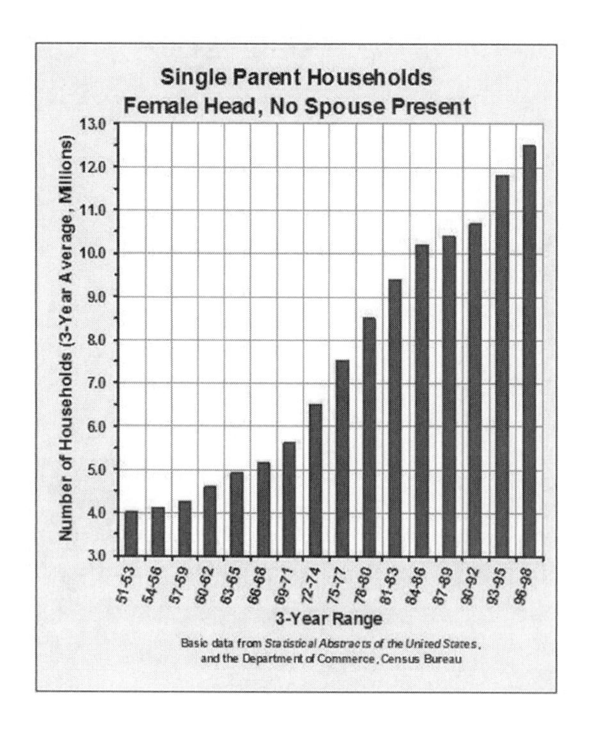
Single Parent Households
Female Head, No Spouse Present
Number of Households (3-Year Average, Millions)
13.0
12.0
11.0
10.0
9.0
8.0
7.0
6.0
5.0
4.0
3.0
51-53
54-56
57-59
60-62
63-65
66-68
69-71
72-74
75-77
78-80
81-83
84-86
87-89
90-92
93-95
96-98
3-Year Range
Basic data from Statistical Abstracts of the United States,
and the Department of Commerce, Census Bureau

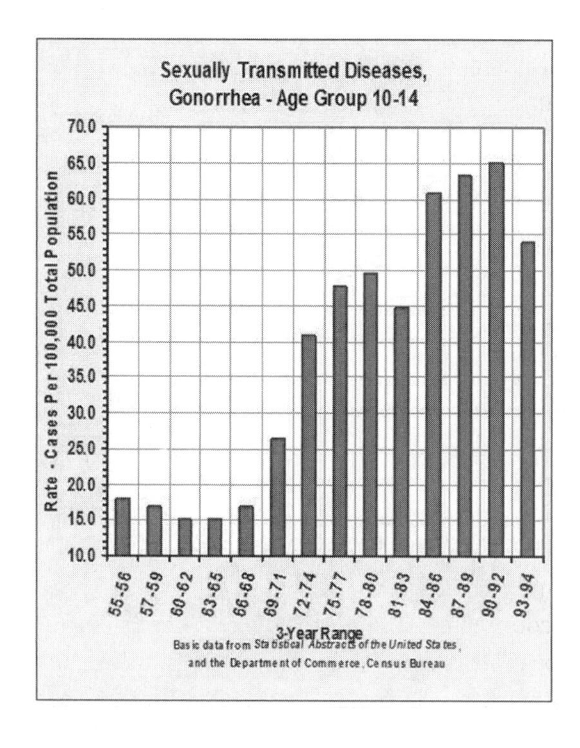
Sexually Transmitted Diseases,
Gonorrhea - Age Group 10-14
Rate - Cases Per 100,000 Total Population
70.0
65.0
60.0
55.0
50.0
45.0
40.0
35.0
30.0
25.0
20.0
15.0
10.0
55-56
57-59
60-62
63-65
66-68
69-71
72-74
75-77
78-80
81-83
84-86
87-89
90-92
93-94
3-Year Range
Basic data from Statistical Abstracts of the United States,
and the Department of Commerce, Census Bureau

is in a curriculum? First, check the sources and origins listed in the curriculum. Do footnotes and curriculum resources cite SIECUS and/or the writings and studies built on the research of Kinsey? Who are the co-authors, or associates? Are they followers of the Kinsey model? A second way is to compare it to the Word of God. How often are sex acts or the genitals referenced in the curriculums and then how often is God's standard of modesty, chastity, self-control and purity mentioned in the same curriculum?

Paul warns us in Colossians 2:8 that you, "See to it that no one takes you captive through hollow and deceptive philosophy which depends on human tradition and the basic principles of this world rather than on Christ." Reformer Martin Luther once commented that, "When the Bible speaks, God speaks," yet many Christians have perhaps unwittingly relied on man's (Kinsey's) philosophy instead of God's revelatory Word when it comes to developing a model of human sexuality.

As a result of all the comprehensive sex education in public schools since 1964, are American children healthier as Kinsey promised? The graphs above deny that possibility. After exposure to any sex education curricula, in or outside of the church, are children more chaste and pure? The failure of the church to slow the flow of gross immorality to our children is in large part due to the silent acceptance of Kinsey's view of sex by the church.

For the sake of our nation and our children, the church must return to the teachings based on the character of God and the revelation of His design. Galatians 6:7 counsels us, "Do not be deceived, God cannot be mocked, for whatever a man sows, that will he also reap."

In the "SIECUS Guidelines" printed under Key Concept 6: Society and Culture, Topic 1: Sexuality and Society, Level 3: it states: "American societal messages about sexuality are often confusing and contradictory. Individuals, (*i.e. children*) need to examine messages received from different sources and establish guidelines for their own behavior.' (*Emphasis added.*)

Contrast that statement with the calling on Christians. We are not to become a law unto ourselves. There is only one "source" used to establish guidelines for behavior, and that is the standard and measure found in God's Word. Proverbs 2:12-15 states: "Wisdom will save you from the ways of the wicked men, from men whose ways are perverse, who leave the straight paths to walk in dark ways, who delight in doing wrong and rejoice in the perverseness of evil, whose paths are crooked and who are devious in their ways."

As a parent, do you struggle with answering questions or broaching the topic of your children's "sexuality?" You have an excellent resource in *Reflections of Moral Innocence*. It was because of this course and it's drastic difference from other Christian sex education curriculums that I was motivated to find out the origins of our current sex education programs. At one time, I was a public health school nurse teaching sex education having no idea of the vast amount of evil connected to the prescribed curriculum I used. Now as a mom, a nurse and public speaker on this topic I would encourage all parents to be in God's Word acting as faithful Bereans. Just because a sex education curriculum claims to be 'Christian' in nature, often it is nothing more than Kinsey philosophy Christianized.

Kinsey's teachings are now part of the moral fiber of our society but the good news is *Reflections of Moral Innocence* is also part of our society. It is the antidote for the Christian family. This course will take you back to the Scriptures and enable you to educate your children in God's standard of chastity, purity, modesty and self control. It is as the cover states: "Leaning to communicate sexual knowledge with dignity."

Additional Resources

by Gary and Anne Marie Ezzo

LET'S ASK AUNTIE ANNE (THE SERIES)

In this series of books we depart from our traditional method of dialectic instruction, (premise, facts, argument and conclusion) and turn to an older and more personal style of persuasion—sharing parenting principles in story-form. Who doesn't love a good story? Stories are entertaining and provide a unique conduit for dispensing practical wisdom and moral truth that otherwise might be lost in an academic venue. When we read or hear a story we find ourselves feeling for the characters through their speech and thoughts. We often identify and empathize with their fears, hopes, dreams and expectations. Most importantly, from their successes and failures we can learn lessons for life. Stories have the power to change us—and indeed they do!

The *Let's Ask Auntie Anne* series consist of five stories and five pertinent parenting themes. Each story is embedded with practical advice that will guide the reader to greater understanding of the complexities of child rearing and hopefully serve as a friend to motivate positive change. The beautiful, historical City of Charleston, South Carolina, frames the backdrop for the series. Auntie Anne draws her parenting lessons from the city's rich history and the daily life of people living on or near the Carolina saltwater marshes. Charleston's glorious past from the Colonial period through the American Revolution, the Civil War, and into the present day and the beauty of its perfectly maintained historical district, cobblestone streets and waterfront parks are all woven into Auntie Anne's lessons.

The descriptions of places, people, scenes, and the anecdotal stories in each book are factual. Apart from Auntie Anne, the characters in our stories are fictional but their needs accurately reflect the many common concerns and challenges for today's parents. The authors speak through Auntie Anne's life story to satisfy the needs of each inquiring couple. Come visit with Auntie Anne. Here you will find a friend, one who connects for a new generation of parents the descriptive—the way it was and the way it is—with the prescriptive—the way it should be.

In Book One, Mac and Vicki Lake can not figure out why their children act as if they are not loved. Mom and Dad are missing something so basic that even the simple phrase "I love you" falls short of its intended meaning. How well did Auntie Anne help them? You decide after reading *How to Raise a Loving Child.*

In Book Two, meet Bill and Elaine Lewis. Who doesn't know at least one family facing the frustration of irresponsible children? Messy rooms, wet towels on the floor, and unfinished homework are just the beginning. Join Bill and Elaine as they go with Auntie Anne on a journey to the heart of *How to Raise a Responsible Child.*

In Book Three, little do Rick and Lela Harvey know that a lack of security is the root of their children's behavioral problems. Nervous, irritable children acting out at school in seemingly uncontrollable ways are a dead giveaway. Auntie Anne's has a plan for this home. Find out what and who needs to change in *How to Raise a Secure Child.*

In Book Four, Clarke and Mia Forden seek out Auntie Anne's advice on building trusting relationships. For Clarke and Mia, the pace of today's family is troubling. How will fathers capture the hearts of their children with so little time? Find out what they wished they had learned a dozen years earlier in *How to Raise a Trusting Child.*

In Book Five, Geoff and Ginger Portier tell their story of how Auntie Anne taught them how to make virtues and values real in the lives of their children. What will it take to create a love for moral beauty within the heart of their children? Auntie Anne provides solid answers in *How to Raise a Moral Child.*

More Resources

by Gary Ezzo, M.A. and Dr. Robert Bucknam, M.D.

With over two million homes to their credit, trusted parenting authors Gary Ezzo and Dr. Robert Bucknam bring their collective wisdom, experience, and insights to bear on this critical phase of growth and development. From first steps to potty training made easy and everything in between, it is all here for you.

ON BECOMING BABYWISE

This book is the first of a six part series that has gained national and international recognition for its immensely sensible approach to parenting a newborn. Coming with the applause of over two million parents and twice as many babies worldwide, *On Becoming Babywise* provides a prescription for responsible parenting. The infant management plan offered by Ezzo and Bucknam successfully and naturally helps infants synchronize their feeding/waketime and nighttime sleep cycles. The results? You parent a happy, healthy and contented baby who will begin sleeping through the night on average between seven and nine weeks of age. Learning how to manage your newborn is the first critical step in teaching your child how to manage his life.

ON BECOMING BABYWISE II

This series teaches the practical side of introducing solid foods, managing mealtimes, nap transitions, traveling with your infant, setting reasonable limits while encouraging healthy exploration and much more. You will learn how to teach your child to use sign language for basic needs, a tool proven to help stimulates cognitive growth and advance communication. Apply the principles and your friends and relatives will be amazed at the alertness, contentedness and happy disposition of your toddler.

ON BECOMING TODDLERWISE

There is no greater fulfillment a parent can receive than the upturned face of a toddler, eyes speaking wonders and a face of confidence in discovering a brand new world with Mom and Dad. In just over a year, the helpless infant emerges as a little moving, talking, walking, exploratory person marked by keen senses, clear memory, quick perceptions and unlimited energy. He emerges into a period of life know affectionately as the Toddler Years. How ready are you for this new experience? The toddler years are the learning fields and you need a trustworthy guide to take you through the unfolding maze of your child's developing world. *On Becoming Toddlerwise* is a tool chest of workable strategies and ideas that multiplies your child's learning opportunities in a loving and nurturing way. This resource is as practical as it is informative.

ON BECOMING POTTYWISE FOR TODDLERS

Potty training doesn't have to be complicated and neither should a resource that explains it. *On Becoming Pottywise for Toddlers* looks to developmental readiness cures of children as the starting point of potty training. Readiness is primary perquisite for successful training according to best selling authors, Gary Ezzo and Pediatrician Robert Bucknam. While no promise can be made, they can tell you that many moms successfully complete their training in a day or two, some achieve it literally in hours. What makes the developmental readiness approach work so successfully?

<u>Timing</u>: Learning to recognize the optimal window for potty training your toddler.

<u>Education</u>: Learning the most effective way to teach your toddler the potty training process.

Motivation: Learning how to instill into your toddler a sustained excitement about using the potty on his or her own.

This resource is filled with time test wisdom, workable solutions and practical answers to the myriad of questions that arise during training.

ON BECOMING PRESCHOOLWISE

Who can understand the mind of a preschooler? You can! Know that above all else, a preschooler is a learner. His amazing powers of reasoning and discrimination are awakened through a world of play and imagination. Through home relationships, he learns about love, trust, comfort, and security; through friends he learns to measure himself against a world of peers; and through unconditional love, a child establishes his own unique selfhood. The growth period between ages three and five years is all about learning, and *On Becoming Preschoolwise* is all about helping parents create the right opportunities and best environment to optimize their child's learning potential. Now influencing over two million homes world-wide, trusted parenting authors Gary Ezzo and Dr. Robert Bucknam once again bring their collective wisdom, experience, and insight to bear on this critical phase of preschool training. From teaching about the importance of play to learning how to prepare a preschooler for the first day of school, from organizing your child's week to understanding childhood fears and calming parental anxiety, sound advice and practical application await the reader. You will find this resource as practical as it is informative, curative as much as it is encouraging.

ON BECOMING CHILDWISE

Ready! Set! Grow! You became a parent overnight...but it takes much longer to become Childwise. Just when you master the baby stage, greater challenges arise. Intellect, self-awareness, curiosity, and social roles are emerging-requiring consistent, caring guidance from you. Equip yourself with more than fifteen Childwise principles for training kids in the art of living happily among family and friends. Foster the safe, secure growth of your child's self-concept and worldview. *On Becoming Childwise* shows you how to raise emotionally balanced, intellectually assertive, and morally sensible children. It's the essential guidebook for the adventurous years from toddler to grade-schooler!

ON BECOMING PRETEENWISE

The middle years, eight to twelve years of age, are perhaps the most significant attitude-forming period in the life of a child. It is during this time that the roots of moral character are established. From the foundation that is formed, healthy or not-so-healthy family relationships will be built. These are the years when patterns of behavior are firmly established patterns that will impact your parent-child relationship for decades to come. Rightly meeting the small challenges of the middle years significantly reduces the likelihood of big challenges in the teen years. In other words, the groundwork you lay during your child's middle years will forever impact your relationship even long after he or she is grown. Included are discussions related to the eight major transitions of middle years children including how to create a family-dependent and not a peer-dependent child. How to lead by your relational influence and not by coercive authority. What discipline methods work and what methods do not work and how to recognize if your child is in trouble.

ON BECOMING TEENWISE

Why do teenagers rebel? Is it due to hormones, a suppressed primal desire to stake out their own domain, or a natural and predictable process of growth? To what extent do parents encourage or discourage the storm and stress of adolescence? *On Becoming Teenwise* looks at the many factors that make living with a teenager a blessing or a curse. It exposes the notions of secular myth and brings to light the proven how-to applications of building and maintaining healthy relationships with your teens. Whether you worry about your teen and dating or your teen and drugs, the principles of *On Becoming Teenwise* are appropriate and applicable for both extremes and everyone in between. They do work!